C000177440

BRAIN ACADEMY
Quests

MISSION
FILE 3

Penny Hollander,
Jenny Plastow,
Louise Moore and
Richard Cooper

Consultant for NACE:
Sue Mordecai

nace

RISING ★ STARS

Rising Stars are grateful to the following people for their support in developing this series: Julie Fitzpatrick, Johanna Raffan and Belle Wallace

NACE, PO Box 242, Arnolds Way, Oxford, OX2 9FR
www.nace.co.uk

Rising Stars UK Ltd, 22 Grafton Street, London W1S 4EX
www.risingstars-uk.com

Published 2005
Reprinted 2005
Text, design and layout © Rising Stars UK Ltd

Editorial Consultant: Sue Mordecai
Design: Hart McLeod
Illustrations: Cover and insides – Sue Lee / Characters – Bill Greenhead
Cover Design: Burville-Riley

British Library Cataloguing in Publication Data.
A CIP record for this book is available from the British Library.

ISBN: 1-905056-34-6

Printed by Vincenzo Bona, Turin

CONTENTS

Welcome to Brain Academy!

Welcome to Brain Academy! Make yourself at home. We are here to give you the low-down on the organisation — so pay attention!

It's our job to help Da Vinci and his colleagues to solve the tough problems they face and we would like you to join us as members of the Academy. Are you up to the challenge?

Da Vinci
Da Vinci is the founder and head of the Brain Academy. He is all seeing, all thinking and all knowing — possibly the cleverest person alive. Nobody has ever actually seen him in the flesh as he communicates only via computer. When Da Vinci receives an emergency call for help, the members of Brain Academy jump into action (and that means you!).

Huxley
Huxley is Da Vinci's right-hand man. Not as clever, but still very smart. He is here to guide you through the missions and offer help and advice. The sensible and reliable face of Brain Academy, Huxley is cool under pressure.

Dr Hood
The mad doctor is the arch-enemy of Da Vinci and Brain Academy. He has set up a rival organisation called DAFT (which stands for Dull And Feeble Thinkers). Dr Hood and his agents will do anything they can to irritate and annoy the good people of this planet. He is a pain we could do without.

Hilary Kumar
Ms Kumar is the Prime Minister of our country. As the national leader she has a hotline through to the Academy but will only call in an extreme emergency. Confident and strong willed, she is a very tough cookie indeed.

General Cods-Wallop
This highly decorated gentleman (with medals, not wallpaper) is in charge of the armed forces. Most of his success has come from the help of Da Vinci and the Academy rather than the use of his somewhat limited military brain.

Mrs Tiggles
Stella Tiggles is the retired head of the Secret Intelligence service. She is a particular favourite of Da Vinci who treats her as his own mother. Mrs Tiggles' faithful companion is her cat, Bond... James Bond.

We were just like you once — ordinary schoolchildren leading ordinary lives. Then one day we all received a call from a strange character named Da Vinci. From that day on, we have led a double life — as secret members of Brain Academy!

Here are a few things you should know about the people you'll meet on your journey.

Echo the Eco-Warrior

Echo is the hippest chick around. Her love of nature and desire for justice will see her do anything to help an environmental cause – even if it means she's going to get her clothes dirty.

Maryland T Wordsworth

M T Wordsworth is the president of the USA. Not the sharpest tool in the box, Maryland prefers to be known by his middle name, Texas, or 'Tex' for short. He takes great exception to being referred to as 'Mary' (which has happened in the past).

Buster Crimes

Buster is a really smooth dude and is in charge of the Police Force. His laid-back but efficient style has won him many friends, although these don't include Dr Hood or the DAFT agents who regularly try to trick the coolest cop in town.

Serena

Serena is a new character to Brain Academy. A time-traveller, Serena knows all about what went on before – and a bit about the future too.

Sandy Buckett

The fearless Sandy Buckett is the head of the Fire Service. Sandy and her team of brave firefighters are always on hand, whether to extinguish the flames of chaos caused by the demented Dr Hood or just to rescue Mrs Tiggles' cat…

Victor Blastov

Victor Blastov is the leading scientist at the Space Agency. He once tried to build a rocket by himself but failed to get the lid off the glue. Victor often requires the services of the Academy, even if it's to set the video to record Dr Who.

Prince Barrington

Prince Barrington, or 'Bazza' as he is known to his friends, is the publicity-seeking heir to the throne. Always game for a laugh, the Prince will stop at nothing to raise money for worthy causes. A 'good egg' as his mother might say.

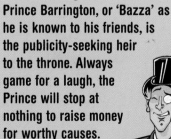

Working with Brain Academy

Do you get the idea? Now you've had the introduction we are going to show you the best way to use this book.

The Quest

This tells you what the quest is about.

MISSION QUEST 3:16

Top of the rocks!

I'm glad you've brought me some rock from Victor's laboratory to study, Buster. Any idea what it actually is?

I don't know, but it looks and feels very strange...

The Quest

Your quest is to help Buster and Da Vinci identify the rocks Victor found on his latest mission to the Planet Xybok. As we currently know more about rocks found on Earth, let's learn more about those first, then we can compare them to the Xybok rocks.

Research Area

Look at the website below to find out about rocks that are found on Earth.
List the characteristics that are used to classify them.

http://www.rocksforkids.com

For more information try pages 46–47.

38

Research Area

Da Vinci will give you some research tips before you start working on the brief.

Each mission is divided up into different parts.

No one said this was easy. In fact that is why you have been chosen. Da Vinci will only take the best and he believes that includes you. Good luck!

Each book contains a number of 'quests' for you to take part in. You will work with the characters in Brain Academy to complete these quests.

The Brief
This is where you try to complete the challenge.

The Brief

Copy the chart below and use it to classify the rocks Victor found. Only you know what they are like and you won't find out about them anywhere else as they are from the Planet Xybok!

- Use the information from your chart to create a poster to tell other people about these rocks.
- Base each of your Xybok rocks on an equivalent Earth rock.
- Illustrate your chart and present your information to the class as a poster.

	Earth name	Colour	Lustre	Shape	Hardness	Special properties
Rock A						
Rock B						
Rock C						
Rock D						
Rock E						
Rock F						

 The study of rocks and minerals is called Geology.

 Don't forget to give your poster a title.

Da Vinci Files

Rocks are used for many things, from making jewellery to constructing buildings.
- Decide what the rocks from Xybok might be suitable for.
- Remember to consider any special properties they have.
- Create an advert for one of the rocks that could be useful to people.
- Name the rocks and give reasons for each name choice.

Da Vinci Files
These problems are for the best Brain Academy recruits. Very tough. Are you tough enough?

PS: See pages 44—47 for a useful process and hints and tips!

Over the desert and far away!

It is time for our trip to Egypt to see the last remaining Seven Wonders of the Ancient World. The journey over the desert will be tough. Tiggles, you and Cods-Wallop will need to be on your toes.

We don't need to move an army, General: it's a sight-seeing trip! We will need to use our intelligence to work out what the difficulties of the journey are before we start to plan, though.

Tanks are always the best vehicles for deserts! It's true they do get rather hot, though!

The Quest

Your quest is to work out as many ways as possible to get to the Pyramids from your school. You could use your own travel experiences to help with the planning, or use travel brochures and guide books to get started.

Research Area

 Try this site to find out about Egypt and the Pyramids:

http://www.ancientegypt.co.uk/pyramids/home.html

There is more information on pages 46–47.

The Brief

 Make a travel itinerary to suit each of the Brain Academy members listed below. To give you some ideas, here is what each one of them enjoys about journeys.

 Da Vinci
Likes time to think and enjoys trying different methods of transport to add to his knowledge.

 Huxley
Likes to get there fast, but can cope with things going wrong.

 Echo
Likes to travel without causing climate disruption, so no aircraft or speedboats!

 Victor
Gets lost easily. Dislikes travel by animal.

 Mrs Tiggles
Prefers reliability, with as few changes as possible. Does not rush. Likes to have meals delivered to her seat.

 You will need to make a comparison of journey times and the travellers' preferences.

People could do one part of a journey, then change to a different method of transport!

Da Vinci Files

Can you suggest three places we could visit next year and give reasons why you think it will suit the Brain Academy members?

Terrific traffic!

This won't do!
There's so much traffic on
the road that everyone's journeys
are taking twice as long. I couldn't
get through the town!

Do you think it's
private cars that are the problem?
Or lorries and vans delivering things
for the shops to sell?

Both, I think.
But you're right, Huxley. We need
to know which is worse so that we can
start putting the situation right.

The Quest

Your quest this time is to help Da Vinci and Huxley
find the answer to their question by surveying your
local traffic, then coming up with some solutions
to the transport crisis! You need to use your computer
to record your data; this will help you keep a check
on environmental conditions.

Research Area

Use this website to get ideas for your survey:
http://www2.youngtransnet.org.uk/portal/essex.asp

For more information try pages 46–47.

The Brief

Use the website to help you set up a survey of traffic in your area.
- Remember, you want to find out what causes more traffic problems – cars, vans or lorries – so make yourself a chart to record the results.
- You will need to look at two things: space on the roads and air pollution.
- What does the town need more of? What should there be less of?

When you have some clear ideas about how to help your town, you will need to write an information sheet on one page of A4, using persuasive language. This should be sent to the children in your school telling them how they can help with traffic problems. They will then need to persuade their parents!

Make three clear suggestions. Ask the children to let you know how they are getting on, by a certain date.

You might want to add a tear-off slip to make it easy for people to get back to you.

Can you find out why traffic is called 'traffic'?

Da Vinci Files

When you have completed your survey and made your information available, contact the environmental department in your local civic centre and let them know what you have done:
- Write them a letter with the results of your survey.
- Include a copy of your information leaflet. Tell them what responses you have had to your tear-off slip.
- Ask for someone to come and speak to your school assembly about traffic in your area.

Make poverty history!

MAKE POVERTY HISTORY

'Make poverty history' is a new concept for the 21st century. When else have the rich helped the poor so much?

I think you need to go back and look at the past, Huxley. If you look at poverty in Tudor times you'll see that they tried to tackle it then, too.

Really! I didn't know that. So maybe there are lessons we can learn from the past to help us become more responsible now.

The Quest

Your quest will take you back in time! Prepare some information charts for Huxley that will help him understand how Tudor society worked, the different groups within it and the responsibilities they each took to make sure that the poor were looked after.

Research Area

Try this site to find out about Tudor Society:

http://historyonthenet.com/Tudors/society.htm

There is more information on pages 46–47.

The Brief

You will need to begin by researching the different lifestyles, houses and clothes for rich and poor in Tudor times:
- Look at the different groups within the rich and find out what they did for charity.
- The poor were also divided into groups. What were they, and how were they helped?

- The information you collect should be word processed and presented in chart form.
- Include some pictures that show the lives, houses and possessions of the different groups within Tudor society.

Don't forget to look at reference books in your school library.

You could also investigate Tudor buildings in your area.

Da Vinci Files

Write a magazine article comparing how we help homeless people today with how the Tudors dealt with vagrants in Elizabethan society. If you were made homeless, when would you prefer to be alive: then or now?

water, water everywhere!

I have been working all night and have made a perfect pump!

Moving water around is usually my department! How does the pump work?

Well, you see, you have to do this, and then this happens, and then...

Oh dear! You're not very good at explaining things, Victor. Can we get some help from the Brain Academy?

The Quest

Your quest is to make a poster to explain what happens at each stage of the pumping process. It needs to be very simple, with few words, so that people can refer to it quickly when they need information on how to use Victor's pump.

Research Area

Look at this amazing water pump from South Africa. It pumps while the children play!

http://www.roundabout.co.za/main_the_playpump.htm

There is more information on pages 46–47.

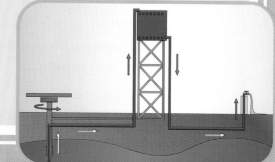

The Brief

Find out how a simple pump works.

- When you are clear about it, make a series of simple drawings showing how you can use the pump to get water up.
- If you can, arrange these into a cycle.
- Write a brief report-style caption (present tense) for each drawing.
- Write each caption on a label.
- Lay the labels next to the drawings and ask a friend to read them to see if your explanation could be improved. Are there any words you don't need?
- Cut out your drawings and stick them carefully in order onto a big piece of brightly-coloured paper.
- Stick each label next to its drawing and display your poster.

The best explanations are the ones that use the least words!

The instructions need to be easy to follow, so you have to set them out well!

Da Vinci Files

When you have finished your task of displaying the instructions for the pump, you need to put your information onto a computer 'database'.

- Open a folder called 'Inventions' and a file called 'Water Pump'.
- Type into the file the instructions for using the pump. Can you do this in no more than fifty words? (Remember: with instructions it helps to use bullet points or numbered stages.)
- Now your instructions are there for Victor to use whenever he gets stuck with his explanation!

Pots and pots of money!

Da Vinci says our pottery business is losing money! We need to sell more pots to keep the studio open.

We need to think what the pots could be used for and what they should be made from!

We're going to need to get a manufacturing team together. Can we get some help with planning this?

The Quest

You need to make lists of all the things pots might be used for, and the things they are made from, and match them together. If you succeed in developing a pottery business plan, the Academy will raise the money for equipment and artist materials. This will form the Brain Academy Pot Catalogue!

Research Area

Conduct your own research at home, in shops, garden centres and public places or using illustrated books.

The Brief

- Start by opening a computer file to record all the containers you see and add a second column for what they contain.
- Create a third column to say why this container is most suitable: does it need to be air-tight? Waterproof? Porous?
- Collect details of about thirty containers of different sizes.

- When you have done this, print your list and highlight any containers which could be made by hand and sold in a gift shop – not plastic, for example.
- Next to your choices, list the materials that would be needed: for example clay, glazes and paint brushes.
- Try to choose containers of different sizes made for a variety of purposes so that the gift-shop can sell as wide a range as possible.

Create a new file on the computer and copy into it the information you already have about your chosen containers. Use it to make a catalogue, explaining how each container is made, the materials used and who could make it.

You should include the dimensions of the container in the catalogue.

Have a look at some store catalogues to give you some ideas for layout.

Da Vinci Files

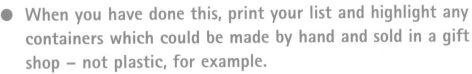

When your catalogue is complete, choose your favourite container and write the instructions for how to make it.
- You may need to look at some websites, or try to visit a potter's studio or a pot-painting studio to get some ideas.
- Set out your instructions as briefly as possible, using numbered stages and writing in the imperative.
- If possible make the pot yourself.

Come in, Planet Xybok

Victor is coming to tell us something about his habit on the Planet Xybok.

The habitat, Wordsworth! He's going to tell us about the habitat and some of the animals on this newly discovered planet.

The Quest

Your quest is to help Victor produce two reports about the habitat on the Planet Xybok. The world's top scientists want to know all about it and as Victor is the only visitor so far, he needs to present his information by comparing it to the habitats we have on Earth.

Research Area

Look at these websites to find out about some of the habitats that we have on our planet. Notice what type of information is included in reports about habitats.

http://www.bbc.co.uk/nature/animals/wildbritain/habitats
http://www.habitats.freeserve.co.uk

There is more information on pages 46–47.

The Brief

Write two reports about the habitat on the Planet Xybok.
Remember this is a newly discovered planet.
- The first report is for people aged 10 and over.
- The second report is for Reception children.
- Use the sample chart below to gather all the information you want to include in your report.

	Temperature	Climate	Plant life	Animals
Earth				
Xybok				

Include as much detail as you can in the first report. Make sure you tell the Reception children all the important points in simple terms.

Illustrations help both younger and older readers understand what you are trying to say.

Da Vinci Files

- Use one of your reports to build a presentation on your computer.
- Show it to the intended audience.
- Listen to their comments and try to improve your report.
- What would you name the plants and animals on Xybok? Give reasons for your suggestions.

A colourful tune

Dr Hood has breached our security and cracked the colour code on our Brain Academy Special Operatives files. We need to give the whole squad a new way to prove their identity!

Let's change our tune and ask them to use a musical note to identify themselves instead!

The Quest

Your quest is to create a musical 'colour code' for the Brain Academy Special Operatives squad. Each agent needs their own unique sound to prove they are who they say they are when they are out in the field.

Research Area

Look at this website to get some ideas on song writing and instrument backing.

http://www.sfskids.org

There is more information on pages 46–47.

The Brief

Fill in the table with the sounds you plan to use for each colour. Write a score for each colour. Each performance must last for at least 10 seconds.

	Instrument	Rhythm	Pitch	Volume
Black				
Blue				
Red				
Brown				
Orange				
Purple				
White				
Yellow				

Test out your code on other team members. How many of your 'sound colours' can they identify correctly?

Da Vinci Files

Prepare instructions for using the sounds and find a way to write your colour code down so General Cods-Wallop's squad can understand the sound and play it.
Create a random score so that the agents can report to HQ on their own or in teams.

Map-a-matics

OK, Bazza and Buckett, we need to map our area to get tourists in to see the views! Coastal cliff-path walks are what we need. Can you get to work while the coast is clear?

There are high cliffs above, so the Fire Service needs to have this information!

I have some land with cliffs on it, too! If you can work out how to do this, I might open my grounds up to tourists as well!

The Quest

You are going to help the team by finding out what maps look like, and getting information on other cliff-path walks to use as a model for the Brain Academy. You may need to show them how it's done, though!

Research Area

Look at Ordnance Survey maps, available free to your school from the LEA. You may need to ask your teacher to help you get these, or perhaps you could do it yourself!

Telephone the Ordnance Survey office on 08456 050505, and ask who is the right person to write or speak to in your LEA. If you cannot do this your local library will have Ordnance Survey maps.

The Brief

- Look at the front of the map to find out what the scale is. This will tell you the size of the squares you see on the map, and how great a distance it represents.
- Draw yourself a grid with squares of the same size.
- Imagine what you think the coastline near the Brain Academy would look like and draw the line of it onto your map grid.
- Have a look at the way the curved contour lines on the Ordnance Survey map show how high the ground is. Put some of these on your map.
- Now look at the key of the Ordnance Survey map. This will show you how roads and railways are drawn on the map, and also how different types of wood and boundary are represented. It will also show you the symbols for different kinds of antiquities.
- Look some of these up on the map using the grid reference – the numbers on each side of the map. The first group of numbers refers to those at the top of the map. The second group of numbers refers to numbers down the side.
- Put numbers on your own map. Then, using coloured pencils, draw in some roads, woods, a park, and other places of interest.
- Make a key for your own map and list the places of interest with their grid numbers.

- Don't forget to mark in the Brain Academy buildings and grounds, with their parklands!

Remember that there will need to be roads or paths going to the places of interest.

Make sure you have marked out the cliff path!

Da Vinci Files

- Once your map is complete you are ready to write some guides for some of the walks on your map.
- Go to http://www.shimbo.co.uk/walking/footpath.htm and look at the information given on one or two of the walks.
- Now you are ready to write a description of some of the walks on your own map of the coastline near the Brain Academy! How many alternative walks of interest can you constuct?

Save our frogs!

We need to save the frog population of France: they are diminishing fast! How can we easily explain their plight in text that can be read by French and English speakers all over the world?

If we put our information onto a diagram, Echo, people could read it even if they weren't very good at either of those languages. Let's hop to it!

What a brilliant idea, Mrs Tiggles. Let's get the Brain Academy Questers involved! And maybe they can tell us what the difference is between a frog and a toad...

The Quest

Your quest is to find out about the life cycle of a frog, and draw a diagram to illustrate this on a large sheet of paper. But – here's the tricky bit – the captions need to be in English and French!

PARIS

Research Area

Look at this website about frogs to get some ideas about the life cycle of a frog:

http://allaboutfrogs.org/weird/general/cycle.html

There is more information on pages 46–47.

The Brief

Use the catalogue in the library to find where the books about amphibians are kept. Amphibians are the group of creatures to which frogs belong.

- Using information from the books or the internet, make a diagram of each stage of the life cycle of a frog.
- Cut out your drawings and stick them onto your large sheet of paper, leaving plenty of room for captions.
- Now write your captions in very simple English. Try to write no more than ten words for each caption.
- Then translate each caption into French using a French/English dictionary.
- Type the bilingual captions into a word-processing document on the computer and print them using blue for English and red for French.
- Cut out and stick them onto your poster in the right places.

Using different colours will help the reader find the information they want more easily!

Lay out all the drawings and captions before you stick them down.

Da Vinci Files

You may be able to help even more by finding out what might be eating the frogs.

- Find out which animals are the predators of frogs.
- Make a list of the predator names — don't forget to translate them into French! — and add them to your 'Grenouille' file!

Harvest festival?

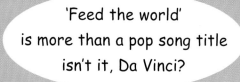

'Feed the world' is more than a pop song title isn't it, Da Vinci?

Yes, 'Give us this day our daily bread' isn't just a Christian concept, Huxley. Millions of people with different religious beliefs or no faith at all believe in this saying.

I wonder how the Brain Academy Questers could demonstrate this at their Harvest Festival celebrations?

The Quest

Within your local community there are Christians, Jews and Muslims who all believe in celebrating the food that we have been given by the Creator God and also sharing what we have with others less fortunate than ourselves. Your quest is to produce a multimedia presentation for all three faith groups to explain the different religious festivals which demonstrate thankfulness for food and sharing with others less fortunate.

Research Area

Look at this website to find out about religious festivals celebrating food:
http://www.woodlands-junior.kent.sch.uk/customs/harvest.html

There is more information on pages 46–47.

The Brief

Your presentation can be a mixture of oral, visual or written parts.
- You could use PowerPoint to present your findings.
- Some appropriate songs and prayers from each of the faiths could also be included.
- Do you want to show examples of foods appropriate to each religion? You could include recipes in the written parts of your presentation.
- Your own reflections, thoughts, artwork and symbols would make the presentation more interesting.
- Think too about timing: how long do you want your presentation to be and do you want to ask your audience any questions?

Maybe you could prepare a simple dish that would be suitable for each religious group.

Did you know that the custom of decorating churches with home-grown produce (what we now call 'Harvest Festival') dates back to 1843!

Da Vinci Files

- Investigate the history of the Christian Harvest Festival and some of the traditions associated with it.
- In groups, write your own Harvest Festival service for the school and compose your own Harvest Festival song to include in the celebrations.

Lucky us?

I've just been reading about the lives of children in Britain during World War II, Da Vinci. I'm glad I didn't live then, as children today are so much better off!

In many ways they are but it was a very interesting and eventful time for the children in the 1940s as well.

Perhaps I need to give this some more thought...

The Quest

Let's give Huxley a more balanced view of what it was like to be a child during the Second World War. Your quest is to present a balanced argument comparing life for children during World War II and the 21st Century. You will need to talk about both the positive and negative elements for each time. You may wish to include some artefacts and first-hand memories from adults who were children during World War II.

Research Area

Can you speak to people who were children in the War? They would be between 65 and 80 years old by now.

Otherwise, use this website to start your thinking about World War II.
http://www.bbc.co.uk/history/ww2children/

There is more information on pages 46–47.

The Brief

When gathering your research information it will be easier if you do it in sections and make a comparison chart.

- Put notes under each section with references for pictures if you need them.
- Are there any other categories you could search under?

Area of research	WWII	21st Century	Your comments
Homes			
Clothes			
Food			
Entertainment			
Toys and games			

Your own comments are an important part of this.

Yes, it will help you to think clearly about the arguments you are going to present to Huxley.

Da Vinci Files

- Compile a list of books/websites about children in World War II to build up a bibliography to support your project.
- You could rate the information in your bibliography by giving stars for the most interesting or useful resources.
- Use your school library and ask teachers for good fiction or reference books as well as researching on the internet.

Christmas card questions

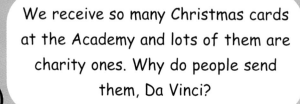
We receive so many Christmas cards at the Academy and lots of them are charity ones. Why do people send them, Da Vinci?

That's easy, Sandy! It's all about celebrating the birth of Jesus... Or is it about holly, robins, snow and good wishes?

Before we send any more cards, let's investigate this tradition together.

The Quest

Find out why people send Christmas cards. Investigate which images, pictures and greetings are the most popular and inform a charity of your results. This could assist them in future design work and ensure they raise more money for their charity.

Research Area

Have a look at different Christmas cards on this site:
http://www.christmas-cards.org.uk

For more information try pages 46–47.

The Brief

- Find as many different pictures and messages from Christmas cards as you can and then group them into types.
- Draw up a questionnaire so you can research which images people prefer to send and to receive.
- Choose 10–15 people to answer your questions (children and/or adults).
- Record their responses and review the results.

- Analyse the answers to find the most frequently given reasons for sending Christmas cards, the most popular designs and greetings and what percentage of your interviewees send charity Christmas cards.
- Publish your findings as an information leaflet which could be sent to a charity of your choice to help them in making future decisions about designs they could use.

Don't forget to ask about the words inside the cards and include those that have a Bible verse.

How many different charities produce Christmas cards?

Da Vinci files

Design your own Christmas card and greeting, which represents what Christmas means to you.

- You may have several different ideas so you could design more than one card.
- Give a presentation to the rest of the class about your choice.
- Adapt your card for a celebration from another religion, such as Hannukah or Chinese New Year.
- Do the Australians design Christmas cards that show sunny beaches?

Sprucing up the Brain Academy

The most famous landscape gardener ever was called 'Capability' Brown, because he saw the 'capabilities' in any landscape. Let's use his ideas to change the gardens of the Brain Academy!

Bazza, did you know that 'Academy' means 'a garden to think in'? But are we capable enough to complete this quest?

Oh yes! We could make the Academy look like Blenheim Palace! Or Warwick Castle! Capability Brown designed those!

The Quest

Your quest is to research Capability Brown's life in the Eighteenth Century and uncover the ideas that led to his great success. Use this information to help persuade Da Vinci that Mrs Tiggles' garden idea will be worth investing in.

Research Area

Use your browser to look up websites for Warwick Castle, Blenheim Palace and Stourhead. All of these gardens were designed by Capability Brown.

For more information try pages 46–47.

The Brief

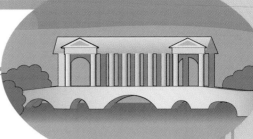

Go to the best website for each of the three gardens and find images that you can print.
- Look through them and see what you can find out about Capability Brown's ideas.
- Why did he like to use water in gardens?
- Why did he think it was a good idea to have different places where you could stand to look out at the gardens?
- Which countries gave him ideas?

Now, plan a letter to persuade Da Vinci that a beautiful garden designed using the ideas of Capability Brown would be of benefit to the Brain Academy.
- Use what you know about persuasive techniques in writing but keep your letter to a maximum of one hundred words.
- Use the images you have chosen to support your argument.
- When you know what you want your garden to look like, write a final copy of your letter, laying it out carefully.

Gardens and natural surroundings send positive messages to your brain!

The sounds of water and bird-song are very soothing and help you to think creatively!

Da Vinci Files

Huxley would like to take a section of the grounds to use ideas by an architect called Edwin Lutyens, who worked with a garden designer called Gertrude Jekyll.
Can you find any images of houses and gardens by Lutyens and Jekyll for Huxley to use?

A slippery slope!

Now that I have installed the world's largest diamond at the top of my new glass mountain, its rightful owners will never see it again!

Da Vinci, I'm relying on the Academy to get that diamond back.

The Quest

Right, Questers, your task is to find a way to climb to the top of the glass mountain and get the diamond back. You should consider the surface of the slope and the type of equipment you will need to complete this task.

Research Area

Look at this website to find out about climbing slippery surfaces and jot down any ideas that might be useful:

http://www.macmountaineering.co.uk

You can find more information on pages 46–47.

The Brief

Build a model of a smooth-sided mountain (you could use a cone made from a plastic sheet).

● Use your model to demonstrate how you could get to the top of the mountain.

● Make sure you can't be seen by Dr Hood and his D.A.F.T. agents.

If the mountain is made of glass it must be really smooth.

Think how you would move something up a window.

Da Vinci Files

List all the other possible methods of getting the diamond back. Be as creative as you can.

● How do people get around the outside of tall glass buildings?

● How do they keep the windows clean?

who is this 'Jesus'?

Da Vinci, I've just read an amazing story! The hero was an ordinary man, with no prospects, who changed the world!

Are we talking about a story from 2000 years ago? If so, it can only be about one man, Victor, Jesus of Nazareth.

You're right. He seems to have been a real revolutionary. Let's investigate further!

The Quest

You are going to works as a history detective, finding out the truth about the life of Jesus and separating the facts from the fiction. What evidence do we have for his existence? Can you find out more through looking at written documents, archaeology and art? Look at what his claims were and think about how he influences the lives of people today.

Research Area

Refer to the Gospels of Matthew, Mark, Luke and John in the New Testament.

A useful book is Jesus through Art by Margaret Cooling (ISBN 1-85175-119-X) The following website contains a whole section on the life and teaching of Jesus:
http://www.request.org.uk

There is more information on pages 46-47.

The Brief

You are going to act out a courtroom scene in which you will give evidence for what you have found about the life and work of Jesus. Your research will need to be divided into different sections and include:

- details of his place of birth, parents, occupation;
- eyewitness accounts from the followers of Jesus;
- later historical accounts from historians like Josephus;
- archaeological finds;
- artists' pictures at different times.

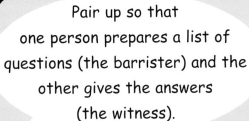

Pair up so that one person prepares a list of questions (the barrister) and the other gives the answers (the witness).

I wonder what people in other countries think about Jesus. Can you find out?

Da Vinci Files

Design a stained glass window depicting your favourite story about Jesus. You can either draw your design and paint in the 'glass' pieces or make a collage from tissue paper.

- To make the collage, draw your design onto thin card.
- Carefully cut out the sections of 'glass' and then stick pieces of tissue paper to the back of the 'lead' framework.
- When you turn your artwork the right way around and hang it up in a window, you will see the light flooding through your very own stained glass window.

Top of the rocks!

I'm glad you've brought me some rock from Victor's laboratory to study, Buster. Any idea what it actually is?

I don't know, but it looks and feels very strange...

The Quest

Your quest is to help Buster and Da Vinci identify the rocks Victor found on his latest mission to the Planet Xybok. As we currently know more about rocks found on Earth, let's learn more about those first, then we can compare them to the Xybok rocks.

Research Area

Look at the website below to find out about rocks that are found on Earth.
List the characteristics that are used to classify them.

http://www.rocksforkids.com

For more information try pages 46–47.

The Brief

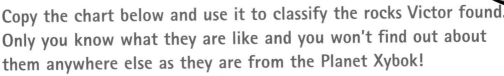

Copy the chart below and use it to classify the rocks Victor found. Only you know what they are like and you won't find out about them anywhere else as they are from the Planet Xybok!

- Use the information from your chart to create a poster to tell other people about these rocks.
- Base each of your Xybok rocks on an equivalent Earth rock.
- Illustrate your chart and present your information to the class as a poster.

	Earth name	Colour	Lustre	Shape	Hardness	Special properties
Rock A						
Rock B						
Rock C						
Rock D						
Rock E						
Rock F						

The study of rocks and minerals is called Geology.

Don't forget to give your poster a title.

Da Vinci Files

Rocks are used for many things, from making jewellery to constructing buildings.

- Decide what the rocks from Xybok might be suitable for.
- Remember to consider any special properties they have.
- Create an advert for one of the rocks that could be useful to people.
- Name the rocks and give reasons for each name choice.

Floodlight fiasco!

It's the annual Brain Academy 5-a-side football match and both teams are raring to go. The winners will receive the prestigious BA Cup from Da Vinci! Let's meet the teams:

The President's Men
M T Wordsworth (Capt.), Blastov, Cods-Wallop, Crimes, Barrington (Goalie)

The Kumar Kats
Kumar (Capt.), Echo, Buckett, Serena, Tiggles (Goalie)

The current holders are the Kumar Kats after a dramatic finish to last year's final. The game ended in controversy when, in the last seconds, with the match poised at 3-3, Tex Wordsworth found himself clean through on goal. Unfortunately for Tex he didn't realise it was his own goal as he blasted the ball past the furious Prince Barrington.

This year, desperate to make amends, Tex has promised his team-mates that he'll 'score lots of runs'.

Hilary Kumar has prepared her team well. They've spent the last two weeks training at the local gym. It is building up to be a classic encounter.

Anyway, the teams are all set, so let's get on with the game!

BANG!

BANG!

POP!

Oh no! The floodlights have exploded... and the BA Cup... it's gone! I bet this is the work of Dr Hood and the D.A.F.T. agents. We need those lights fixed; and quick. It's time to call the Academy!

Can you shed some light on the problem, Da Vinci?

Get Serena to work on this one. She'll reveal the solution.

Research Area

Back in the days of the Renaissance, in the 16th Century, there were no electric lights. All we had were candles and oil lamps. The winter evenings were very long...

Look at this website to investigate the types of lights that are available today.
http://www.electriclightcompany.co.uk/acatalog/index.html

For more information go to pages 46–47.

CONTINUE ➡

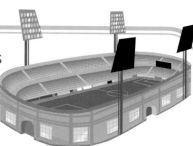

Your brief is as follows:

Build a set of FOUR floodlights to light up a (model) football stadium. You must be able to turn the lights on and off.

To achieve this you will need to:
- Talk to your teacher about safety issues. Do NOT go near a mains plug.
- Make a simple circuit with a battery, bulb, switch and connecting wire.
- Explore different ways to make a switch using simple classroom materials. Some switches you can press and some you can slide.
- Investigate which materials could be used to reflect light. Floodlights have to shine over a large area so they need reflectors.

Materials to use:

- Batteries
- Bulbs
- Bulb holders
- Connecting wire
- Switches
- Tape
- Aluminium foil
- Small mirrors
- Lolly-sticks or balsa wood
- A large shoe box for the model stadium
- Paint for decoration

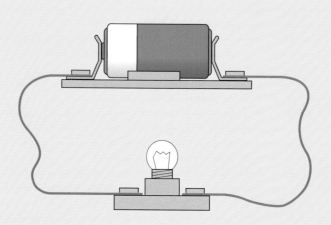

Da Vinci Files

How illuminating, Serena. Once the lights are back on we'll be able to catch those pesky D.A.F.T. agents, get the BA Cup back and play the match.

You will have your own designs but you could build one like this.

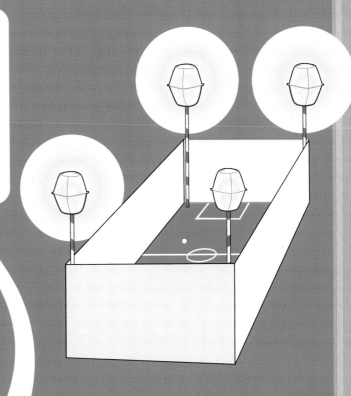

Make a labelled plan of your stadium before you start.
- Draw the circuit diagram.
- Decide on the type of switch you will use.
- List all your materials.
- Evaluate your stadium. Is the 'pitch' lit up?
- Can you turn the floodlights off and on?
- Can you improve your floodlight system?

Thank you for your help. We will use your model as a template for building a new floodlight system for the Cranium Stadium. In the meantime, I'm off to play an important match. Come on you Kats!

The TASC Problem Solving Wheel
TASC: Thinking Actively in a Social Context

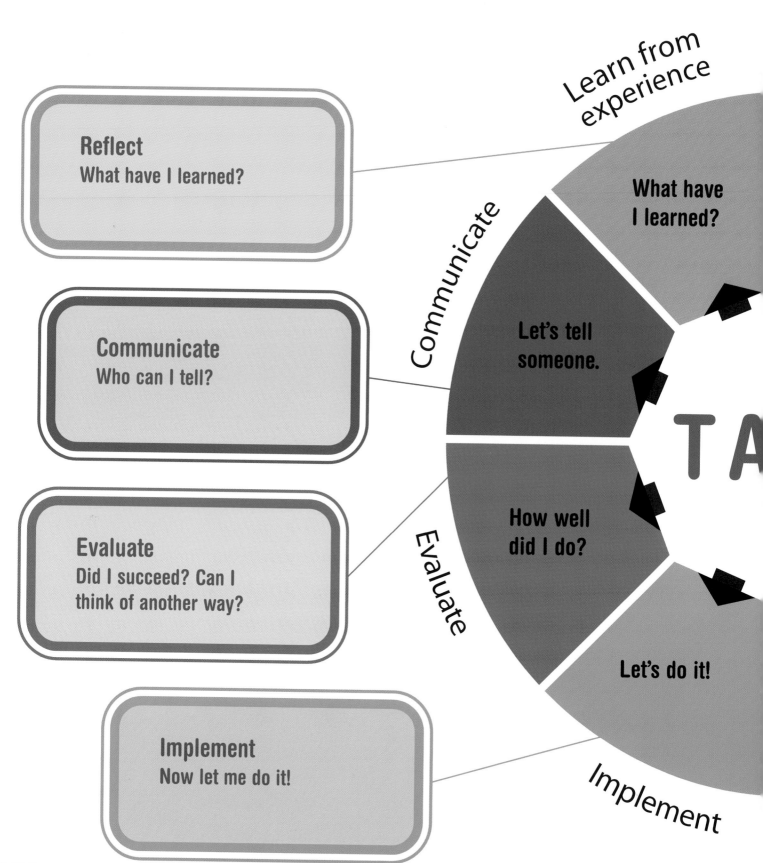

Reflect
What have I learned?

Communicate
Who can I tell?

Evaluate
Did I succeed? Can I think of another way?

Implement
Now let me do it!

Learn from experience

Communicate

What have I learned?

Let's tell someone.

How well did I do?

Evaluate

Let's do it!

Implement

TA

We can learn to be expert thinkers!

Gather/organise

What do I know about this?

Identify

What is the task?

Generate

How many ideas can I think of?

Decide

Which is the best idea?

TASC

Gather/organise
What do I already know about this?

Identify
What am I trying to do?

Generate
How many ways can I do this?

Decide
Which is the best way?

The Quest Online Library

Mission Quest 3.1
For more information try:
http://www.zyra.org.uk/pyramids.htm
You could also use atlases and globes or try reading this book: Horrible Histories – The Egyptians (Scholastic Publishers)

Mission Quest 3.2
For more information try:
http://www.walkingbus.com/

Mission Quest 3.3
For more information try:
http://wwwhistorylearningsite.co.uk/poor_in_elizabethan_england.htm
http://www.tudorbritain.org/life
http://www.4learning.co.uk/essentials/history/units/tudor_bi.shtml

Mission Quest 3.4
For more information try:
http://www.oxfam.org.uk/what_we_do/where_we_work/india/cleanwaterkashmir.htm

Mission Quest 3.5
Use your web browser to look up your nearest pottery café or look in the Yellow Pages telephone directory to find one where you can practise making your own pots.

Mission Quest 3.6
For more information try:
http://www.habitats.freeserve.co.uk

Mission Quest 3.7
For more information try:
http://www.ngfl-cymru.org.uk/vtc-home/vtc-ks2-home/vtc-ks2-music-composing
http://www.creatingmusic.com

Mission Quest 3.8
Ordnance Survey website has details of 'Free Maps' service:
http://wwwordnance survey.co.uk/freemapsfor11yearolds/.
Alternatively there is an online 'Get a map' service:
http://ordnancesurvey.co.uk/oswebsite/getamap

Mission Quest 3.9
For more information try:
http://www.zephyrus.co.uk/lifeofthefrog.html
Any books giving clear information on frogs.

Mission Quest 3.10
For more information try:
http://www.reonline.org.uk
http://www.request.org.uk

Mission Quest 3.11
For more information try:
http://www.bbc.co.uk/history/war//wwtwo/index.shtml
http://www.wartime-memories.fsnet.co.uk/2ww
How they lived: A Schoolchild in World War II by Miriam Moss (Wayland)
ISBN 1-85210 -201-2

Mission Quest 3.12
For more information try:
http://www.request.org
http://www.livaudaisnet.com

Mission Quest 3.13
For more information try:
http://www.gardenvisit.com/b/brown1.htm
http://www.capability-brown.org.uk/gardens/gardens.htm

Mission Quest 3.14
For more information try:
http://www.terrifictoy.com/store/tree_frog.html
http://www.xs4all.nl/~ednieuw/Spiders/InfoNed/sensoryleg.html

Mission Quest 3.15
For more information try:
http://www.rejesus.co.uk
http://www.webjesus.co.uk/basics/onelife.htm

Mission Quest 3.16
For more information try:
http://www.minsocam.org
http://www.sdnhm.org/kids/minerals

SUPERQUEST / Mission Quest 3.17 - 18
For more information try:
http://www.thelightingcentre.co.uk/

nace

What is NACE?

NACE is a charity which was set up in 1984. It is an organisation that supports the teaching of 'more-able' pupils and helps all children find out what they are good at and to do their best.

What does NACE do?

NACE helps teachers by giving them advice, books, materials and training. Many teachers, headteachers, parents and governors join NACE. Members of NACE can use a special website which gives them useful advice, ideas and materials to help children to learn.

NACE helps thousands of schools and teachers every year. It also helps teachers and children in other countries, such as America and China.

How will this book help me?

Brain Academy books challenge and help you to become better at learning by:
* thinking of and testing different solutions to problems;
* making connections to what you already know;
* making mistakes and learning from them;
* working with your teacher, by yourself and with others;
* expecting you to get better and to go on to the next book;
* learning skills which you can use in other subjects and out of school.

We hope that you enjoy the books!

Write to **RISING STARS** and let us know how the books helped you to learn and what you would like to see in the next books.

Rising Stars Ltd, 22 Grafton Street, London W1S 4EX